The Legend of Sleepy Hollow

Washington Irving

HELBLING LANGUAGES

www.helblinglanguages.com

The Legend of Sleepy Hollow
by Washington Irving

First published 2010

ISBN 978-3-85272-230-6

The publishers would like to thank the following for their kind permission to reproduce the following photographs and other copyright material: Wikipedia/public domain p6.

Series editor Maria Cleary
Adapted by Janet Olearski
Illustrated by Giuseppe Palumbo
Activities by Janet Olearski
Design and layout by Pixarte
Printed by Athesia

About this Book

For the Student

Listen to the story and do some activities on your Audio CD

Talk about the story

jug• When you see the orange dot you can check the word in the glossary

For the Teacher

Go to our Readers Resource site for information on using readers and downloadable Resource Sheets, photocopiable Worksheets, Answer Keys and Tapescripts. Plus free MP3 sample tracks from the story.

www.helblingreaders.com

For lots of great ideas on using Graded Readers consult Reading Matters, the Teacher's Guide to using Helbling Readers.

Level 4 Structures

Sequencing of future tenses	*Could / was able to / managed to*
Present perfect plus *yet, already, just*	*Had to / didn't have to*
First conditional	*Shall / could* for offers
Present and past passive	*May / can / could* for permission
	Might for future possibility
How long?	*Make* and *let*
Very / really / quite	Causative *have*
	Want / ask / tell someone to do something

Structures from lower levels are also included.

Contents

About the Author

Washington Irving was born into a rich Scottish family in New York in 1783. He studied law but literature was his real passion. While he was working as a lawyer•, he started to write for newspapers and magazines. His articles and stories satirized• the customs• and manners• of the Americans. New York was home to many Dutch settlers• and Irving wrote about them in his first book *A History of New York*, published in 1809. This humorous account by a fictional• character called Diedrich Knickerbocker was immensely successful and was described as 'the first great book of comic literature written by an American'.

In 1815 Irving moved to England to look after the family company, but the business was not a success and he returned to his writing. His most famous stories, *The Legend of Sleepy Hollow* and *Rip Van Winkle*, appeared in 1819. The popularity of these books made Irving a celebrity in Europe and America.

He lived in London, Paris and Madrid, writing stories, essays and history books, such as *Tales of a Traveller, The Life and Voyages of Christopher Columbus, The Conquest of Granada, Tales of the Alhambra*. He returned to New York in 1832 but ten years later he went back to Madrid in a diplomatic role•. He spent his last years in America, in Tarrytown in the valley of Sleepy Hollow where he wrote *The Life of George Washington*. He died there in 1859 at the age of 76.

Glossary

- **customs:** habits
- **diplomatic role**: he was American Minister for Spain
- **fictional:** not real
- **lawyer:** person who looks after legal things
- **manners:** way they behaved and lived
- **satirized:** made fun of (in an ironic way)
- **settlers:** people who move to live in another country or colony

About the Book

The Legend of Sleepy Hollow (1809) tells the story of a schoolteacher from Connecticut, Ichabod Crane, who comes to the small village of Sleepy Hollow. When he meets Katrina Van Tassel, the pretty daughter of a wealthy farmer, he falls in love. But he has a rival, the boastful• Brom Bones. After a party at her house, Katrina rejects Ichabod's courtship• and he rides home dejected•. On the way back he encounters the terrifying Headless Horseman, the ghost of an enemy soldier from the **Revolutionary War**•. A frightening chase ensues and Ichabod disappears. The people of Sleepy Hollow believe that Ichabod's ghost now haunts the village.

The narration runs on various levels. The main story is presented as an authentic account found among the papers of the narrator, Diedrich Knickerbocker, a fictional Dutch historian. The stories about the war, ghosts and superstitions are told by the villagers. We know also that Ichabod reads some frightening stories from his favourite book, ***A History of New England Witchcraft***.

The Legend of Sleepy Hollow is an early example of American fiction. It explores the themes typical of the **newborn nation**•: greed for money and possessions in a country rich in natural resources, physical mobility in a vast continent where people can travel to seek• their fortune, the survival of the European heritage, the memory of the war still fresh in people's minds and their attachment to the superstitions and beliefs of the past.

- **boastful**: vain; praising himself
- **courtship:** period when you convince someone to love and marry you
- **dejected:** sad
- **newborn nation**: the birth of America was marked by the Declaration of Independence on 4 July 1776.
- **Revolutionary War**: the American War of Independence (1775–1783) in which thirteen American colonies fought against Great Britain.
- **seek:** look for

Before Reading

1 Match the words and the pictures.

a) ☐

b) ☐

c) ☐

d) ☐

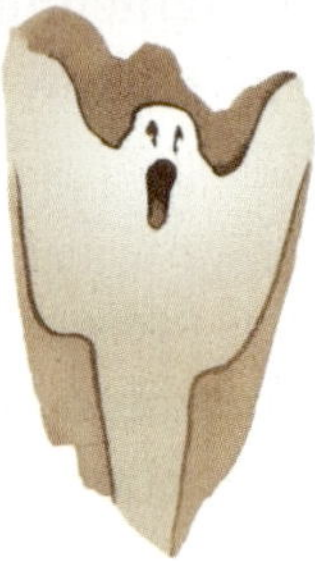

e) ☐

f) ☐

1) ghost 2) dragon 3) giant 4) witch
5) goblin 6) headless horseman

2 Complete the sentences with the words above.

a) A .... mixes ingredients in a big pot or cauldron to make magic potions.

b) A .... is huge. It has got wings and a long tail.

c) .... is an enormous person.

d) The .... was killed on the battlefield and his ghost still rides his horse.

e) A .... appears after death and usually haunts old castles.

f) A .... is a bold little creature that plays tricks on people.

3 **Look at these pictures from the story. Write six questions about them. Exchange questions with your partner. Write answers to your partner's questions. Keep your answers in a safe place until after you read the story.**

WEB **4** **You are going to read about the following places in the story. Do some research on the Internet and write a sentence about each of them.**

Tarry Town   The Hudson River   Sleepy Hollow

5 **What do you think *'The Legend of Sleepy Hollow'* will be about? Tick (✓) the boxes below.**

a) ☐ A place where people keep falling asleep.
b) ☐ A poor man who becomes rich.
c) ☐ A ghost story.
d) ☐ A war story.
e) ☐ A story about love and romance.
f) ☐ A story about people who tell stories.

Before Reading

2 **1 Here are the pictures of three characters from the story. Listen to their descriptions and number the pictures.**

a) ☐

Brom Van Brunt

b) ☐

Ichabod Crane

c) ☐

Baltus Van Tassel

2 Think about the following and answer the questions.

a) Which of these things is **not** usually in a classroom?

1 ☐ copybooks 3 ☐ inkstands 5 ☐ a desk
2 ☐ books 4 ☐ a mirror 6 ☐ windows

b) Which of these is **not** a farmer's job?

1 ☐ take the horses to water 4 ☐ make hay
2 ☐ cut wood for the winter fire 5 ☐ mend fences
3 ☐ drive the cows from pasture 6 ☐ rock a cradle

c) Which animal is **not** usually found in a farmyard?

1 ☐ pig 3 ☐ pigeon 5 ☐ goose
2 ☐ ostrich 4 ☐ turkey 6 ☐ hen

d) Circle two items you can wear on your head.

coat stockings breeches cap gown
petticoat straw hat shoes dress buttons

3 Match the words from the story with the pictures.

a) crane c) beehive e) cradle g) fiddle

b) logs d) scarecrow f) pumpkins h) sword

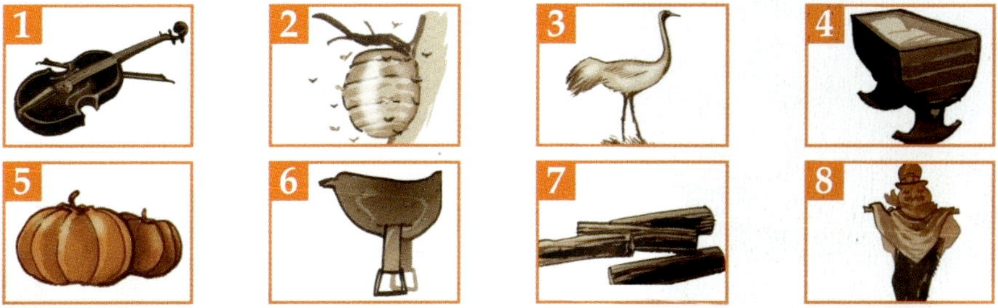

4 Use each of these words to complete the following sentences.

a) The teacher's clothes fluttered in the wind, frightening the birds, so that from a distance he looked like a ....

b) The musician played his .... and everyone danced.

c) Since Ichabod was tall, but extremely thin, with narrow shoulders, people thought he looked like a ....

d) Ichabod sat for hours with a child on one knee and rocking a baby in a .... at the same time with one foot.

e) Mrs Van Tassel was a good cook and she could make tasty pies from ....

f) The bees lived in a large .... at the bottom of the garden.

g) Ichabod's schoolhouse was one large room, built with .... from the forest.

h) While Ichabod was riding the .... slipped from under him.

A QUIET VALLEY

3 *The following account• was found among the papers of the late• Diedrich Knickerbocker.*

On the eastern shore of the Hudson River there is a small town called Greensburgh. This place is better known as Tarry Town. It was given this name by the wives of that area because on market days their husbands 'tarried,' or wasted time, at the local tavern•. I cannot confirm this myself but I mention• it just to be precise.

There is a little valley surrounded by high hills about two miles from here. This is one of the quietest places in the whole world. A small stream glides• through it so silently that it could lull• one to sleep. Only the sound of the birds ever interrupts this tranquility.

I remember that, when I was very young, I once wandered into a grove• of trees. It was noon, when all nature is strangely quiet. The trees shaded one side of the valley. I couldn't think of a better place than this little valley where I could escape from the world and its distractions, and quietly dream away the remnants• of a troubled• life.

Glossary

- **account:** story; report
- **glides:** runs or moves smoothly
- **grove:** small wood
- **late:** dead
- **lull:** relax
- **mention:** say
- **remnants:** the remainder; what is left
- **tavern:** an inn or bar where people can eat and drink
- **troubled:** difficult; with problems

COUNTRY LIFE AND CITY LIFE

Do you live in the country or in a city?
Where would you prefer to live – the countryside or the city? Why?

Because of the lazy atmosphere of the place and the character of its inhabitants, who are descended from the original Dutch settlers, this valley has been known for a long time by the name of Sleepy Hollow•. The young men who live here are called the Sleepy Hollow Boys. A drowsy•, dreamy influence seems to hang over the land. Supposedly, a German doctor put a spell• on the place during the early days of the settlement.

According to another story an old Indian chief held his powwows• here. Certainly something seems to have cast• a spell over the minds of the good people. They have all kinds of strange beliefs. They go into trances•, have visions, frequently see strange sights, and hear music and voices in the air. The whole neighborhood is full of stories of superstitions• and haunted• places.

However, one dominant spirit haunts this magical region. It is the apparition• of a figure on horseback, without a head. Some people think it is the ghost of a soldier whose head was carried away by a cannon ball in a battle during the Revolutionary War. The local people often see him hurrying along in the dark of night. He haunts not just the valley, but the adjacent roads and a nearby church.

Glossary

- **apparition:** something that appears
- **cast:** (here) put
- **drowsy:** sleepy
- **haunted:** inhabited by ghosts
- **hollow:** valley
- **powwows:** meetings of Native Americans
- **spell:** magic formula
- **superstitions:** beliefs in unreal things
- **trances:** states like sleep

According to historians the soldier's body was buried in the churchyard and his ghost now rides to the scene of battle in a nightly search for his missing head. It seems he sometimes rushes with great speed through the Hollow because he is in a hurry to get back to the churchyard before daybreak.

This legend has provided material for many wild stories, and at all the country firesides he is known by the name of the Headless Horseman of Sleepy Hollow.

THE HEADLESS HORSEMAN

How did the horseman lose his head?
Which places does he haunt?
What is he searching for?
When must he return to the churchyard?

THE SCHOOLMASTER

4 It is not just the local people who imagine things. Everyone who comes to live in the area is affected. However wide awake they were before they arrived in this sleepy region, they soon inhale the magic influence of the air and begin to imagine things. In these little Dutch valleys everything stays the same. It has been many years since I visited Sleepy Hollow, but I'm sure everything has remained exactly as it was.

Around thirty years ago, a man from Connecticut by the name of Ichabod Crane stayed or, as he expressed it, 'tarried' in Sleepy Hollow, for the purpose of instructing the children of the neighborhood. The surname of Crane suited him. He was tall, but extremely thin, with narrow shoulders, long arms and legs. His hands dangled a mile out of his sleeves, and his feet were like shovels. His head was small and flat on the top. He had huge ears, large green glassy eyes, and a long nose. If you saw him striding across a hill on a windy day, with his clothes fluttering around him, you could have mistaken him for a scarecrow.

His schoolhouse was one large room, constructed from logs. The windows were partly glazed, and partly covered up with pages from old copybooks. When not in use, the room was locked by twisting a twig in the handle of the door, and by leaning stakes against the window shutters.

Glossary

- **crane:** a type of large bird with very long legs
- **dangled:** were hanging loosely
- **fluttering:** moving in the air
- **glazed:** containing or made of glass
- **inhale:** breathe in
- **logs:** pieces of wood cut from trees
- **scarecrow:** figure that scares birds in a field
- **shovels:** tools for digging
- **stakes:** wood cut from trees
- **striding:** walking; taking long steps
- **twig:** small branch

It was easy for a thief to get in, but it was likely to be difficult for him to get out again. The schoolhouse was in a lonely but attractive location at the foot• of a woody hill. There was a stream close by with a large birch• tree growing at one end.

From there the low murmur of his pupils' voices, studying their lessons, could be heard on drowsy summer days, like the hum of a beehive. This was interrupted now and then by Ichabod's authoritative• voice, speaking in a tone of menace•, or by the terrible sound of the birch, as he encouraged some tardy loiterer• to move along the flowery• path of knowledge. I am not saying that he was a cruel man. On the contrary, he only used the birch on the real troublemakers•. He never punished anyone without assuring him afterwards, 'you will remember and thank me for this as long as you live.'

SCHOOL

What is your school like?
How many classrooms are there?
Have you got a library, a sports hall or a swimming pool at your school?
Do you have lunch at school? If so, where do you eat?
How many students are there at your school?

Glossary

- **authoritative:** able to control others
- **birch:** tree (Ichabod uses its branches as a stick)
- **flowery:** (here) rich
- **foot:** (here) bottom
- **menace:** threat
- **tardy loiterer:** a slow person; someone who wastes time
- **troublemakers:** people who caused problems

When school was over, he usually accompanied some of the smaller boys home if they had pretty sisters, or if their mothers were good cooks. He took care to be on good terms with his pupils. The revenue• from his school was small, and it was scarcely enough to feed him. He ate a lot and though he was thin he had the dilating• powers of an anaconda•.

To help out with his maintenance, he lived and ate at the houses of the farmers whose children he taught. He lived a week at a time with each family, thus going the rounds• of the neighborhood with all his worldly belongings tied up in a cotton handkerchief.

So that this was not too costly for his patrons, who considered the cost of schooling a heavy burden•, he made himself useful. He helped the farmers with light work, helped to make hay, mended fences, took the horses to water, drove the cows from pasture•, and cut wood for the winter fire. He found favor in the eyes of the mothers by being nice to the children, particularly the youngest. He sat for hours with a child on one knee, rocking a cradle• at the same time with his other foot.

Ichabod was also the neighborhood singing master and earned a few shillings by instructing the children to sing hymns•. On Sundays, he went to church with his group of chosen singers, and his voice resounded• far above the rest of the congregation•.

- **anaconda:** snake
- **burden:** weight; responsibility
- **congregation:** people in a church
- **cradle:** baby's bed
- **dilating:** expanding; growing larger
- **going the rounds:** moving around
- **hymns:** religious songs
- **pasture:** fields
- **resounded:** was heard
- **revenue:** money; earnings

A MAN OF LETTERS

5 A schoolmaster is generally a man of some importance in female circles•. He is considered to be a kind of idle• gentleman, with taste and accomplishments• superior to those of the rough country boys. Our man of letters enjoyed the smiles of all the young country ladies. Between church services on Sundays, he was the centre of their attention, gathering grapes for them from the vines in the churchyard and reading aloud for their amusement the epitaphs• written on the tombstones. Sometimes he walked along the bank of the pond with a whole bevy• of them. The shy country boys hung back•, envying• his superior elegance and style of conversation.

Ichabod was a kind of travelling newspaper. He carried the local gossip from house to house so his appearance was always greeted with satisfaction. The women regarded him as a man of great learning because he read books all the way through, and he was an expert in Cotton Mather's book 'History of New England Witchcraft•,' in which, by the way, he firmly• believed.

POPULARITY

Why do you think Ichabod is so popular?
What advice can you give to someone who wants to be popular?

Glossary

- **accomplishments:** achievements; skills
- **bevy:** group; crowd
- **circles:** (here) groups
- **envying:** jealous of
- **epitaphs:** things written on grave stones
- **firmly:** very much; strongly
- **hung back:** did not join in
- **idle:** lazy; someone who doesn't work
- **witchcraft:** the practice of magic and casting spells

He was both crafty and credulous. No tale was too monstrous for him to believe. After school he loved to stretch himself out on the bank of the stream by his schoolhouse and read old Mather's frightening tales until the arrival of evening made the printed page a mist before his eyes. Then, as he walked home through woods to the farmhouse where he was staying, every little sound at that witching hour stirred his imagination and frightened him.

On such occasions, either to stop himself from thinking or to drive away evil spirits, he sang hymns. As the good people of Sleepy Hollow sat by their doors in the evening, they were often surprised to hear him singing on a distant hill or on the dark road.

Ichabod spent the long winter evenings with the old women, listening to their tales of ghosts and goblins. As they sat spinning by the fire, they told him about haunted fields, and haunted streams, and haunted bridges, and haunted houses, and particularly about the Headless Horseman of the Hollow.

In return he entertained them with his stories of witchcraft. He frightened them with tales about omens and terrible sights and sounds, and speculation about the significance of certain comets and shooting stars. He enjoyed all this while he was sitting comfortably by the fire, but then he paid for it when he had to walk home alone.

- **bank:** side of a river
- **crafty:** clever in a dishonest way
- **credulous:** believing; trusting
- **goblins:** ugly evil beings
- **omens:** signs that something bad is going to happen
- **speculation:** guessing; supposition
- **spinning:** making wool
- **stream:** small river
- **witching:** magical; a time when strange things happen

Everywhere he saw fearful shapes in the ghastly• glare• of the snowy night. Every shrub• covered with snow looked like a ghost waiting for him on the path. He was terrified by the sound of his own steps. He dreaded• to look over his shoulder in case he saw somebody walking close behind him. Whenever the wind howled through the trees, it seemed to him to be the galloping• horseman on one of his nightly rides.

Daylight put an end to all these evils. But, then, one day Ichabod's path was crossed by a being• who causes more trouble to mortal man than ghosts, goblins and an entire race of witches. That being was a woman.

Glossary

- **being:** person
- **dreaded:** was afraid
- **galloping:** moving quickly on a horse
- **ghastly:** terrible
- **glare:** brightness
- **shrub:** small bush

THE RICH FARMER'S DAUGHTER

6 Among the musical pupils who came one evening a week for instruction was Katrina Van Tassel. She was the only child of a well-off• Dutch farmer. She was a fine healthy girl of eighteen, plump• and rosy-cheeked, like one of her father's peaches. She was also a bit of a flirt•, which you could tell from the way she dressed. She wore ornaments of pure gold, and her petticoat• was short so that she showed off the prettiest foot and ankle in the countryside. Ichabod Crane had a soft and foolish heart towards young women so it is not surprising that such a tasty morsel• soon found favor in his eyes.

Katrina's father, old Baltus Van Tassel, was only concerned with his own farm, where everything was snug• and happy. He did not lead an extravagant life but he had everything he needed.

His home was on the banks of the Hudson, in a green and fertile place. An elm tree spread its branches over a spring of the sweetest water. Close to the farmhouse there was a vast barn and every corner of it seemed to burst with the treasures of the farm. Swallows and martins• flew twittering around the eaves•, and rows of cooing pigeons enjoyed the sunshine on the roof. Fat pigs grunted in the comfort of their pens•. There were geese in the pond and turkeys, cockerels and hens in the farmyard.

- **eaves:** part of the roof of a house
- **flirt:** someone who likes to play and joke with the opposite sex
- **pens:** areas surrounded by a fence
- **petticoat:** under skirt
- **plump:** a little fat
- **snug:** confortable
- **swallows and martins:** types of birds
- **tasty morsel:** something delicious to eat
- **well-off:** rich

Ichabod's mouth watered as he looked at this rich promise of luxurious winter food. He imagined pigeon pie, geese in gravy, and ducks in dishes, covered in onion sauce. Instead of the pigs he saw slices of bacon, and juicy ham. Instead of turkey he saw a roast bird with a necklace of savory sausages.

Ichabod rolled his great green eyes over the fat meadow lands, the rich fields of wheat, of rye, of buckwheat, of Indian corn, and the orchards full of fruit, which surrounded Van Tassel's home, and his heart longed for the young woman who was to inherit these lands. He imagined selling everything, and investing the money in land. He imagined himself married to Katrina and with a whole family of children, all of them traveling in a wagon loaded with household items. He saw himself riding a fine horse, setting out for a new life in Kentucky, Tennessee – or who knows where!

When he entered the house, the conquest of his heart was complete. It was a spacious farmhouse, with a sloping roof, built in the style of the first Dutch settlers. Farming and fishing equipment was stored under the eaves of the house. There was a spinning wheel at one end of the house, and a churn at the other, showing the different uses to which the porch was put.

Glossary

- **buckwheat:** grain
- **churn:** large container for making butter
- **gravy:** a sauce for meat
- **longed for:** desired; wanted
- **porch:** covered area on the front of a house
- **rye:** grain
- **savory:** flavoured with salt and spices
- **sloping:** inclined; not horizontal
- **spinning wheel:** 

In the hall, arranged on a dresser•, there were rows of glittering• pewter•. In one corner stood a huge bag of wool ready to be spun. In another corner, cloth, Indian corn, and dried apples and peaches, hung in sacks along the walls. Through the open parlor door he saw carved chairs, and dark wood tables shining like mirrors. Colored birds' eggs were suspended above the mantelpiece•, a great ostrich egg was hung from the centre of the room, and a cupboard displayed silver ornaments and china• plates.

LOVE

Do you think Ichabod has fallen in love with Katrina?
Why does he want to marry her?

- **china:** fine ceramic
- **dresser:** a cupboard in which plates are stored (see illustration)
- **glittering:** shining
- **mantelpiece:** the shelf above a fireplace
- **pewter:** a type of grey-coloured metal

From the moment Ichabod laid his eyes on the house and its contents, he lost his peace of mind. His only thought was how to gain the affections of Van Tassel's daughter. This posed • more difficulties than those encountered • by a knight in a fairytale.

A knight only had to deal with • giants, witches and dragons. It was easy to defeat all of these. He only had to reach the castle dungeon •, where the lady of his heart was imprisoned. A knight could do this as easily as cutting into a pie, and then the lady gave him her hand as a matter of course •.

Ichabod, on the contrary, had to win the heart of a spoilt • young country girl, whose whims • were always presenting him with new difficulties. He had to meet real flesh and blood • rivals, her many admirers, who opened every door to her heart, who watched each other angrily and who were ready to take action against any new competitor.

Glossary

- **as a matter of course:** automatically
- **deal with:** face; defeat
- **dungeon:** underground prison
- **encountered:** met
- **flesh and blood:** real (of people)
- **posed:** made
- **spoilt:** with too many things and attention
- **whims:** unusual wishes and desires

THE RIVAL

7 The most impressive of these was a strong, energetic young man, called Abraham or, according to the Dutch abbreviation, Brom.

Brom Van Brunt was a local hero. The countryside was full of stories of his feats • of strength. He was broad-shouldered and agile, with short curly black hair. His face was not unpleasant, with a mixed expression of fun and arrogance. People gave him the nickname of Brom Bones because of his Herculean • frame • and powerful limbs •. He was famous for his great knowledge of horsemanship, and was as skillful • on horseback as a Tartar •. He always won races and cock • fights, and because of his strength he was the judge in all disputes •. No one ever argued against his decisions.

Brom was a rough type but he was good-humored. He had three or four close companions, who regarded him as their model. With them he traveled around the countryside getting into fights or having a good time. In cold weather he always wore a fur cap with a fox's tail, and when people spotted this hat from a distance, among a group of horse riders, they knew a storm • was coming. Sometimes his gang rode past the farmhouses at midnight, whooping and shouting. Old ladies, startled • out of their sleep, exclaimed, 'There goes Brom Bones and his gang!'

- **cock:** male hen
- **disputes:** fights; arguments
- **feats:** difficult acts
- **frame:** body; structure
- **Herculean:** like Hercules
- **limbs:** arms and legs
- **skillful:** good
- **startled:** surprised
- **storm:** trouble
- **Tartar:** horse rider from Mongolia

The neighbors regarded him with a mixture of awe•, admiration, and good-will. Whenever any prank• or brawl• occurred in the vicinity, they always shook their heads, and agreed that Brom Bones must be the cause of it.

Brom chose the beautiful Katrina as the object of his attention. Though his romantic advances were more like those of a bear, Katrina did not completely discourage his hopes. When Brom's horse was seen tied up outside Van Tassel's house on a Sunday night, it was a sure sign that its master was inside courting• Katrina. All other suitors• passed by in despair without stopping. They didn't want to upset• a lovesick• lion.

This was the formidable• rival with whom Ichabod Crane was in competition. Braver men avoided contests like these. Wiser men despaired• of them. But in his character Ichabod had a mixture of flexibility and perseverance•. Though he bent, he never broke, and though he bowed beneath the slightest pressure, the moment the pressure was off, he stood up straight and carried his head as high as ever.

It was madness for him to compete openly with his rival. Ichabod did not like to be beaten in love, so he made his advances in a quiet and crafty manner. As a singing master, he made frequent visits to the farmhouse. There was no need for him to worry about interference from the parents, which is so often a obstacle in the path of lovers.

Glossary

- **awe:** amazement
- **brawl:** fight
- **courting:** visiting her romantically
- **despaired:** gave up hope
- **formidable:** to be feared
- **lovesick:** sick from being so in love
- **perseverance:** determination
- **prank:** trick; joke
- **suitors:** men who wanted her
- **upset:** make angry

Baltus Van Tassel was an easy-going man. He loved his daughter even better than his pipe and, like a reasonable man and an excellent father, he let her do anything she liked. His wife had enough to attend to in the house and farmyard. As she wisely observed, ducks and geese are foolish and must be looked after, but girls can take care of themselves.

PARENTS

What qualities must a mother and a father have to be good parents?
Are Baltus and his wife good parents?
Do you have any special advice for them about Katrina?

So, while Katrina's mother worked at her spinning wheel at one end of the porch, Baltus sat smoking his pipe at the other. In the meantime, Ichabod sat with Katrina by the side of the stream under the great elm, or strolled• with her in the twilight•, that hour so favorable to romance.

I admit I do not know how women's hearts are wooed• and won. To me they have always been a mystery. Some seem to have only one door of access•, while others have thousands, and can be captured in many different ways. From the moment Ichabod Crane made his advances, Brom Bones seemed to lose interest. His horse was no longer seen tied up outside the house on Sunday nights, and a deadly• feud• gradually arose between him and the schoolmaster.

- **access:** way to enter
- **deadly:** terrible
- **feud:** serious argument
- **strolled:** walked slowly
- **twilight:** time between day and night
- **wooed:** convinced to fall in love

Brom liked the idea of settling• their dispute over the lady in combat•, like the knights of old. But Ichabod was too conscious of his opponent's superior strength to enter into a fight with him. He was not going to give him any opportunity to try.

Brom found Ichabod's pacifism• very irritating. He had no alternative but to think up some unpleasant practical joke to play on his rival. Ichabod became an object of persecution• for Brom and his gang. Until this time his life was very peaceful, but now they caused him all kinds of trouble. They blocked the chimney of his school so that it filled with smoke. They broke in• at night, in spite of Ichabod's clever security precautions, and turned everything topsy-turvy•. The poor schoolmaster began to think all the witches in the country held their meetings there.

PRACTICAL JOKES

What is a practical joke? What practical jokes did Brom and his friends play on Ichabod?
Have you ever played a practical joke on anyone? What did you do?

Brom took every opportunity to ridicule• Ichabod in Katrina's presence. He even taught a dog to whine•, and introduced it as a rival of Ichabod's who was there to instruct her in hymn singing. This went on for some time without either of them winning.

Glossary

- **broke in:** entered without permission
- **in combat:** by fighting
- **pacifism:** non-violence
- **persecution:** cruel treatment
- **ridicule:** make fun of
- **settling:** solving
- **topsy-turvy:** in disorder
- **whine:** make a high-pitched crying noise made by an animal

AN INVITATION

8 One autumn afternoon Ichabod was sitting in his classroom watching his students at work when the silence was interrupted by the arrival of one of Van Tassel's servants. He came riding up to the school door with an invitation for Ichabod to attend a party that evening at Van Tassel's house.

The schoolroom was now full of noise and activity. The students were rushed through their lessons. Those who were fast managed to get through their lesson without being punished. Those who were slow got a smack• on their rear• to speed them up or help them understand a long word.

Books were thrown aside without being put away on the shelves, inkstands• were upset•, benches were pushed over, and the whole school was turned loose• an hour before the usual time. The students burst out of the schoolhouse and onto the grass like an army of young imps•, yelping• and making a racket•.

Ichabod spent an extra half hour getting ready, brushing dust off his best black suit – indeed, his only black suit - and combing his hair in the schoolhouse's broken old mirror. He wanted to appear before Katrina in the true style of a cavalier so he borrowed• a horse from the farmer with whom he was lodged•, an old Dutchman called Hans Van Ripper.

- **borrowed:** took (for the night)
- **imps:** naughty fairies
- **inkstands:** small containers for ink
- **lodged:** staying
- **racket:** noise
- **rear:** bottom
- **smack:** they were hit
- **turned loose:** sent home
- **upset:** knocked over
- **yelping:** making noises like a dog

He made his way to the party on horseback like a knight in search of adventure.

It is only fair to give you a true description of my hero and his horse. The animal he was riding was a broken-down bad-tempered• work horse. He was thin and ugly. His head was shaped like a hammer•. His mane and tail were tangled• and full of burs•. He was blind in one eye and that eye seemed to look angrily at you, while the other eye had the look of a devil in it. He was called Gunpowder and, judging by that name he once must have been a very ferocious animal. In fact he once was a favorite horse of his master Van Ripper, who was a mad horse rider. Very probably some of Van Ripper's own spirit was infused into the animal. Gunpowder looked old and broken-down, but in reality he had an evil character inside him.

Ichabod rode with short stirrups•, which brought his knees nearly up to the top of the saddle. His sharp elbows stuck out like a grasshopper•'s legs. He carried his whip vertically in his hand and, as his horse jogged• on, the motion of his arms was a bit like the flapping of a pair of wings. A small wool hat rested on the top of his nose, and the skirts of his black coat fluttered out almost to the horse's tail. Such was the ridiculous appearance of Ichabod and his horse.

As Ichabod rode, he thought of all the delights of autumn: the apples made into cider•, the corn made into cakes, the pumpkins made into delicious pies, and the buckwheat made into breads. Katrina, with her delicate little hands, was going to cover those breads with butter and honey specially for him.

Glossary

- **bad-tempered:** angry
- **burs:** sticky seeds or bits of plants
- **cider:** a drink made from apples
- **grasshopper:** jumping insect with long legs
- **jogged:** traveled with a regular up and down movement
- **hammer:** 
- **stirrups:** metal supports where riders place their feet when sitting on a horse
- **tangled:** knotted; twisted

His head was full of sweet thoughts like these as he travelled along the hillside overlooking the Hudson River. As the sun set, just a few amber• clouds floated in the sky, without a breath of air to move them. The golden horizon changed gradually into a pure apple green, and from that into a deep blue.

Towards the evening Ichabod arrived at the Van Tassel residence, which he found full of all the best people from the surrounding countryside. There were old farmers wearing homemade coats and breeches•, blue stockings, and huge shoes with magnificent pewter buckles•. Their wives wore caps, long gowns, and homemade petticoats. There were young women, almost as old-fashioned as their mothers, except where a straw hat, a fine ribbon, or perhaps a white dress, gave evidence of city innovation•. The sons wore short coats, with rows of stupendous• brass• buttons, and their hair styled in the fashion of the times.

COLOURS

The author uses different colours and tones to describe people, places and things in the story. What do these colours describe?

- apple green
- black
- golden
- amber
- silver
- white
- deep blue
- blue

Glossary

- **amber:** yellow-brown
- **brass:** bright yellow metal
- **breeches:** old-fashioned trousers to the knee
- **buckles:** ornaments made of metal used to decorate shoes or belts
- **innovation:** new or modern idea
- **stupendous:** amazing; wonderful

Brom Bones, however, was the hero of the scene. He came to the gathering on his favorite horse Daredevil, a creature, like himself, full of mischief•, and which only Brom could control. Brom was, in fact, noted for preferring nasty• animals. His horses played all kinds of tricks and kept the rider in constant risk of breaking his neck. In Brom's opinion, a well-behaved horse was unworthy• of a lad• of spirit.

- **lad:** boy, young man
- **mischief:** naughtiness, bad behaviour
- **nasty:** unpleasant
- **unworthy:** not good enough

THE FEAST

9 When Ichabod entered the Van Tassel mansion he was overcome• by what he saw. He wasn't impressed by the sight of all those beautiful young women, but by the huge display of cakes of various kinds.

There were doughnuts, sweet cakes, shortcake, ginger cakes, honey cakes, and the whole family of cakes. Then there were apple pies, and peach pies, and pumpkin pies. There were slices of ham and smoked beef, and delectable• dishes of preserved plums, and pears, and quinces•, not to mention roasted chickens, together with bowls of milk and cream, all mixed up higgledy-piggledy•. And in the middle of the table sending up clouds of vapor was the teapot. Ichabod Crane managed to do justice to every dainty•.

Glossary

- **delectable:** delicious; tasty
- **higgledy-piggledy:** in confusion; in disorder
- **managed... dainty:** he ate everything, all the rare and expensive food
- **overcome:** (here) impressed
- **quinces:** type of apple

Ichabod's spirits rose when he ate good food. As he ate he could not help looking all around him with large greedy eyes, chuckling• at the possibility that he might one day be lord of all this luxury and splendor. He looked forward to turning his back• on the old schoolhouse, and saying goodbye to Hans Van Ripper, and every other mean person like him.

Old Baltus Van Tassel moved about among his guests with a face full of good humor. He shook hands with his guests, gave them a friendly slap on the shoulder, laughed loudly and invited them to 'carry on• and help yourselves'. The sound of music summoned everyone to the dance. The grey-haired musician's fiddle• was as old and battered• as himself. He played on just two or three strings, accompanying every movement of his bow with a motion of the head, bowing almost to the ground, and stamping with his foot whenever a new couple entered the dance.

Ichabod prided himself on• his dancing as much as his vocal powers•. No part of him was idle. His body was in full motion, clattering• about the room. Everyone, including the farm workers, came to admire him and stood looking with delight at the scene through the open doors and windows. So, this man who usually spent his time beating naughty boys was now animated and joyous. The lady of his heart was his partner in the dance, smiling graciously in reply to all his loving looks. Meanwhile Brom Bones, who was overcome• with love and jealousy, sat brooding• by himself in a corner.

- **battered:** in bad condition
- **brooding:** thinking unhappily
- **carry on:** continue
- **chuckling:** laughing
- **clattering:** moving noisily
- **fiddle:** violin
- **overcome:** (here) full of
- **prided himself on:** felt proud of
- **turning his back on:** leaving
- **vocal powers:** ability to sing

GHOST STORIES

10 When the dancing was over, Ichabod joined some people who were sitting with Van Tassel, gossiping about former times and telling long stories about the war. During the war the British and American lines were close to this neighborhood, so the area was the scene of fighting. Each storyteller exaggerated his story with a little fiction• and, in this way, made himself the hero of every adventure.

There was the story of a Dutchman called Doffue Martling. He nearly captured a British ship except that his gun broke when he fired• it the sixth time. Then there was an old gentleman who, in the Battle of White Plains•, managed to stop a bullet with a small sword. He felt it whizz around the sword, and then bounce off the handle. To prove it he could show them the sword and how it was bent a little at the handle. Several more of these storytellers were equally great on the battlefield. They all thought they played an important role in bringing the war to a happy conclusion.

All these tales were nothing in comparison with the ghost stories that followed. Ghost stories and superstitions live best in sheltered•, long-settled• places like Sleepy Hollow, but they are lost when people move to big villages.

Besides, there is no encouragement for ghosts in most of our villages. By the time they finish their first nap• and turn in their graves•, their surviving friends have travelled away from the neighborhood.

Glossary

- **Battle of the White Plains:** between the British and George Washington's troops on 28 October 1776
- **fiction:** untrue stories
- **fired:** used (a gun)
- **graves:** holes for dead bodies
- **long-settled:** where people stay
- **nap:** short sleep
- **sheltered:** isolated and protected

So, when these ghosts go out for their night walks, they have no friends left to visit.

Several Sleepy Hollow people were present at Van Tassel's house and, as usual, they were busy telling everyone their wild and wonderful ghostly legends.

GHOST STORIES

Why do we find more ghost stories in 'sheltered, long-settled places' than in big towns and villages?

Do you know any ghost stories?

They told many depressing tales about funerals and about wailing• ghosts. They spoke about the woman in white, who haunted Raven Rock, having died there in the snow. They often heard her shrieking• on winter nights before a storm.

• **shrieking:** screaming

• **wailing:** crying out

Most of the stories, however, were about Sleepy Hollow's favorite ghost, the Headless Horseman. They heard him several times, patrolling• the countryside. It was said he tied his horse up every night among the graves in the churchyard.

The church stands on a hill, and this quiet location seems to have made it a favorite haunt• for troubled spirits. A slope descends from the church to a silver sheet of water•, bordered• by high trees. In such a sunny yard, overgrown• with grass, the dead could certainly rest in peace. On one side of the church there was a stream and over the stream there was once a wooden bridge. The road and the bridge itself were shaded by overhanging trees, and these made it a gloomy• place even in the daytime. At night the darkness was terrifying. This was one of the places where people most often met the Headless Horseman.

They told the tale of old Brouwer. All his life he never believed in ghosts, but, returning one night, he met the Horseman. The ghost made him get up behind him on his horse. Together they galloped over bushes and shrubs, over hills and swamps•, until they reached the bridge. At this point the Horseman suddenly turned into a skeleton. He threw old Brouwer into the stream, and in a clap of thunder, he disappeared over the tops of the trees.

Glossary

- **a favorite haunt:** a place they liked to visit
- **bordered:** on the edges/sides
- **gloomy:** dark and sad
- **overgrown:** with too many plants
- **patrolling:** moving around and controlling
- **sheet of water:** a pond or a small lake
- **swamps:** areas of wet land

Brom Bones immediately told a story of his own that was three times as amazing. He described how when he returned one night from a neighboring village, this Headless Horseman overtook him. Brom offered to race with him in order to win a bowl of punch•. He should have won it too because his horse Daredevil easily beat the ghost horse. But just as they came to the church bridge, the Horseman galloped away, and then vanished• in a flash of fire.

The men told these stories to each other as they sat in the dark. From time to time the faces of the listeners were lit by the gleam• of light from someone's pipe. This made a deep impression on Ichabod, who told stories from the work of his favourite author, Cotton Mather. To these he added many remarkable events. Some were stories from his native state of Connecticut, and some described the fearful sights which he experienced in his nightly walks around Sleepy Hollow.

When the party ended, the farmers gathered together their families in their wagons, and were heard for some time rattling• along the roads, and over the distant hills. Some of the ladies sat on horseback behind their favorite young men. Their light-hearted laughter, mixed with the clatter• of hoofs, echoed through the silent woodlands, sounding fainter• and fainter, until they gradually died away.

Soon all was silent and deserted. Only Ichabod remained to have a tête-à-tête• with the heiress•, fully convinced that he was now on the road to success. What happened during this meeting I really do not know. I'm afraid something must have gone wrong, because after just a few minutes Ichabod left, looking quite upset.

Glossary

- **clatter:** sound of metal hitting the road
- **fainter:** less loud
- **gleam:** soft light
- **heiress:** a woman who is going to inherit a lot of money or property
- **punch:** (here) a drink
- **rattling:** sound made by the movement of the wagons
- **tête-à-tête:** private conversation
- **vanished:** disappeared

Oh, these women! These women! Could that girl have used Ichabod? Was her encouragement of the poor teacher all a trick to secure her conquest of• his rival? Heaven only knows!

It's enough to say that Ichabod went straight to the stable and, with several hearty• kicks, woke up his horse from the comfortable bed in which he was soundly• sleeping, dreaming of mountains of corn and oats, and grassy valleys.

DISAPPOINTMENT

What do you think happened between Ichabod and Katrina?
Why was Ichabod upset?
What did Katrina say to him?
Ichabod thought she liked him. Why did she give Ichabod this idea?
Have you ever been disappointed? What happened?

- **hearty:** energetic
- **secure her conquest of:** win
- **soundly:** deeply

SHADOWS

11 It was night and Ichabod travelled home with a heavy heart•. Below him from the hills he saw the dark waters of the river. In the distance he heard a guard dog barking on the opposite shore. Now and then he heard the crowing of a cock from some distant farmhouse. Close by he heard nothing except the occasional sound of a cricket• or a bullfrog•.

All the stories of ghosts and goblins from the afternoon now came back to him. The night grew darker and darker. The clouds hid the stars from his sight. Ichabod never felt so lonely and depressed. In addition he was approaching the very• spot where many of the ghost stories once took place. In the centre of the road stood an enormous tree, which towered like a giant above all the other trees. Its branches were huge and gnarled• and they twisted down almost to the earth, and rose again into the air. This tree was connected with the tragic story of Major André•. In the war they took him prisoner close by and this tree was known as Major André's tree.

As Ichabod approached this fearful tree, he began to whistle•. For a moment he thought his whistle was answered, but it was just the wind sweeping• through the dry branches. As he came a little nearer, he thought he saw something white, hanging in the middle of the tree. He paused and stopped whistling but, when he looked more carefully, he saw that it was a branch of white wood where the tree was hit by lightning.

Glossary

- **bullfrog:** large frog
- **cricket:** insect
- **gnarled:** twisted; not straight
- **Major André:** a British officer in Canada who was taken prisoner by American forces in 1775
- **sweeping:** (here) moving
- **very:** precise; exact
- **whistle:** make sounds by blowing air
- **with a heavy heart:** unhappily

Suddenly he heard a groan•. His teeth chattered•, and his knees knocked against the saddle. But it was only the sound of one huge branch rubbing against another, as they were blown about by the breeze. He passed the tree in safety, but new dangers awaited him.

DANGERS

Is Ichabod in danger?
What is the worst thing that can happen to him now?

About two hundred yards from the tree, a small stream crossed the road. A few rough logs, laid side by side, served as a bridge over this stream. To pass this bridge was the most difficult trial•. Major André was captured at this identical spot. The soldiers who surprised him were hidden under cover of these trees. This stream has always been thought to be haunted, and any schoolboy who has to pass it alone after dark feels very fearful.

As Ichabod approached the stream, his heart began to thump•. However, he summoned• up all his courage, gave his horse a few kicks in the ribs, and attempted to move quickly across the bridge. But, instead of moving forward, the stubborn• old animal moved sideways•, and ran against the fence. Ichabod, whose fears increased with the delay, pulled at the reins and kicked.

Glossary

- **chattered:** (here) knocked against each other quickly
- **groan:** sound made by a person who is sick or in pain
- **sideways:** to the side
- **stubborn:** determined
- **summoned:** collected; gathered
- **thump:** make a loud beating sound
- **trial:** test

It was all useless. His horse started to move, it is true, but he jumped to the opposite side of the road into a thicket• of brambles• and bushes. The schoolmaster now used both his whip and his heels on the ribs of old Gunpowder, who ran forward, snorting•, but came to a halt• just at the bridge, with a suddenness that nearly threw his rider over his head.

Just at this moment Ichabod's sensitive ear heard a noise by the side of the bridge. In the dark shadow on the edge of the stream, he saw something huge and misshapen•. It did not move, and in the darkness it looked like some gigantic monster getting ready to jump on top of him.

The teacher's terrified hair stood up on his head. What was he going to do? It was too late now to turn and run. Besides, a ghost could ride on the wings of the wind. So what chance was there of escaping from it?

Summoning up his courage and stammering•, he demanded•, 'Who are you?' But he received no reply. He repeated his question in an even more agitated• voice. Still there was no answer. Once more he kicked Gunpowder's sides to try and make him move. Then, shutting his eyes, he started to sing a hymn.

- **agitated:** afraid and worried
- **brambles:** plants with thorns
- **demanded:** asked
- **halt:** stop
- **misshapen**: having a strange shape
- **snorting:** pushing air loudly through the nose
- **stammering:** speaking with hesitation and difficulty
- **thicket:** area with trees and bushes

THE CHASE

12 Just then the shadowy shape started to move, and with a leap• it stood in the middle of the road. Though the night was dark and dismal•, the form of the unknown figure could now be seen to some degree. He appeared to be a horseman of massive dimensions•, who was mounted on a powerful-looking black horse. He was neither threatening nor sociable towards Ichabod, but kept to the side of the road, trotting along on the blind side of old Gunpowder, who was recovered now from his fright and misbehavior.

Ichabod did not like this strange midnight companion. He could not stop thinking about Brom's encounter with the Headless Horseman, so he moved his horse faster in the hope of leaving the other rider behind. The stranger, however, also moved his horse faster so that he went at the same speed as Ichabod.

At this point Ichabod slowed his horse down to a walk, intending to try and lag behind•. But, the other rider did the same. Ichabod's heart began to sink•. He tried to continue his hymn, but his parched• tongue stuck to the roof of his mouth. He could not sing a note. The silence of his obstinate companion was very mysterious. The reason for it soon became evident.

They reached higher ground and this brought the figure of his fellow traveller into relief• against the sky. He was gigantic, and wrapped in a cloak, and Ichabod was horrified to see that he was headless! Ichabod's horror increased when he saw that the rider's head was in his hand.

Glossary

- **dismal:** dull and sad
- **Ichabod's heart began to sink:** he started to lose hope
- **into relief:** his outline or shape could be seen clearly
- **lag behind:** stay behind
- **leap:** jump
- **of massive dimensions:** enormous
- **parched:** dry

Ichabod's terror became desperation. He rained• a shower• of kicks and blows on Gunpowder, hoping to give his companion the slip• by a sudden movement, but the ghost took off• with a jump at the same moment. Off they went, the two of them galloping away. Stones flew and sparks• flashed at every stride•. Ichabod's thin clothes fluttered in the air, as he stretched his long body across his horse's head, in his eagerness• to escape.

- **a shower:** (here) many
- **eagerness:** wish; desire
- **give his companion the slip:** escape from his companion
- **rained:** (here) gave many
- **sparks:** small flashes of light
- **stride:** step
- **took off:** suddenly started to run fast

They reached the road which leads to Sleepy Hollow. Instead of going up the road, Gunpowder, who seemed possessed by• the Devil, turned in the opposite direction, and plunged• down the hill. This road leads through a sandy area shaded by trees for about a quarter of a mile, and then it crosses the bridge famous in the ghost story. Just beyond that is the green hill on which the church stands.

Up to now the horse's panic gave his unskillful rider an advantage in the race, but just as he got halfway through the Hollow, the saddle's girth• snapped•, and Ichabod felt the saddle slipping from under him. He seized• the pommel•, and tried to hold it in place, but in vain•. Grabbing old Gunpowder around the neck, Ichabod just had time to save himself before the saddle crashed to the ground, and he heard it trampled• under foot by his pursuer•.

For a moment the terror of Hans Van Ripper's anger passed through his mind, for this was Van Ripper's best Sunday saddle. But this was no time for petty• fears. The ghost was right behind him. He was having trouble staying on the horse's back: sometimes slipping to one side, sometimes to the other, and sometimes bouncing up onto the top of his horse's backbone, with such violence that he thought it was going to break him in half.

He saw an opening in the trees and began to hope that the church bridge was close. He saw the walls of the church under the trees beyond. He remembered the place where Brom Bones's ghostly competitor disappeared. 'If I can only reach that bridge,' thought Ichabod, 'I will be safe.'

Glossary

- **girth:** strap
- **in vain:** without hope; uselessly
- **petty:** small; not important
- **plunged:** moved suddenly down
- **pommel:** handle (on a saddle)
- **possessed by:** taken over; inhabited by
- **pursuer:** the person chasing him
- **seized:** took; grabbed
- **snapped:** broke
- **trampled:** crushed; broken

Just then he heard the black horse panting• close behind him. He was sure he could even feel his hot breath. He gave Gunpowder another kick in the ribs and the old horse jumped up onto the bridge. He thundered• over the wooden planks• and reached the opposite side.

And now Ichabod looked behind him to see if his pursuer was going to vanish, as the legends said, in a flash of fire and thunder. At that moment he saw the spectre• standing up in his stirrups, in the act of throwing his head at him. Ichabod tried to avoid that horrible missile•, but it was too late. It encountered his cranium• with a tremendous crash. He fell headfirst into the dust, and Gunpowder, the black horse, and the ghost rider, passed by like a whirlwind•.

Glossary

- **cranium:** head
- **missile:** flying object
- **panting:** breathing heavily
- **planks:** pieces of wood
- **spectre:** ghost
- **thundered:** moved quickly and noisily
- **whirlwind:** tornado

DISAPPEARED!

13 The next morning the old horse was found without his saddle, and with the bridle under his feet. He was quietly munching• the grass outside his master's gate. Ichabod did not make his appearance at breakfast. The boys gathered at the schoolhouse, and strolled idly along the banks of the stream, but no schoolmaster appeared. Hans Van Ripper now began to feel uneasy• about the fate of poor Ichabod, and his saddle.

An inquiry was set in motion•, and after careful investigation they found his trail. On the road leading to the church they found the saddle trampled into the dirt. The tracks of horses' hoofs were found in the road. Evidently the animals were racing at a furious speed. These tracks were traced to the bridge, beyond which, on the bank of the stream, they found the hat of the unfortunate Ichabod. Close beside it there was a shattered• pumpkin.

The stream was searched, but the body of the schoolmaster was never found. Hans Van Ripper, as executor• of Ichabod's estate•, examined the bundle containing all his worldly effects•. They consisted of two and a half shirts, two scarves, two pairs of socks, an old pair of underpants, a rusty razor•, a book of psalms, and a broken pitch-pipe•. The books in the schoolhouse belonged to the community, except for Cotton Mather's 'History of Witchcraft,' a 'New England Almanac,' and a book of dreams and fortune telling.

- **effects:** belongings; possessions
- **estate:** possessions and property
- **executor:** the person responsible for a dead person's things
- **munching:** chewing; eating
- **pitch-pipe:** a musical instrument
- **razor:** sharp thing to cut beards, etc.
- **set in motion:** started
- **shattered:** broken
- **uneasy:** worried

Inside this last book there was a sheet of paper. On the paper, in honor of Van Tassel's daughter, were Ichabod's scribbled• verses. The books and the poetic scrawl• were immediately burned by Hans Van Ripper.

From that moment, Van Ripper decided not to send his children to school any more, observing that he never knew any good to come of this reading and writing nonsense. The schoolmaster received his pay just a day or two before. He must have been carrying all his money at the time of his disappearance.

The mysterious event caused much speculation at the church the following Sunday. Gossips collected in the churchyard, at the bridge, and at the spot• where the hat and the pumpkin were found. The stories of Brouwer, Bones, and many others were remembered. People shook their heads, and came to the conclusion that Ichabod was carried off by the Headless Horseman. As he was a bachelor•, and owed no money, nobody worried any more about him. The school was transferred to a different area of the town, and another teacher took over•.

ICHABOD'S FATE

Do you think that Ichabod was carried off by the Headless Horseman?
If Ichabod is alive, why doesn't he return to Tarry Town?
What will happen to Katrina? And to Brom Bones?

Glossary

- **bachelor:** single man
- **scrawl:** untidy writing
- **scribbled:** written untidily
- **spot:** place
- **took over:** came and took control

A LONG TIME AFTER

14 It is true that an old farmer who went to New York on a visit several years after, and who provided this account of the ghostly adventure, brought home the information that Ichabod Crane was still alive.

Apparently he left the neighborhood partly through fear of the ghost and Hans Van Ripper, and partly because he was so upset by Katrina's rejection. It seems that he moved to a distant part of the country, that he taught at a school and studied law at the same time, that he was admitted to the bar•, became a politician, electioneered•, wrote for the newspapers and, finally, became a judge.

Brom Bones, who shortly after his rival's disappearance led Katrina in triumph to the altar•, looked very knowing• whenever the story of Ichabod was told. He always burst into a hearty laugh when the pumpkin was mentioned. Some people suspected that he knew more about the matter than he chose to tell.

- **electioneered:** campaigned; became a political candidate
- **knowing:** that he knew something about it
- **led Katrina in triumph to the altar:** married
- **was admitted to the bar:** qualified as a lawyer

The old women, however, maintain to this day that Ichabod was spirited away• by supernatural means•, and it is a favorite story often told around the fire on winter evenings. The bridge became more than ever an object of superstitious awe.

The schoolhouse soon fell into decay•, and was reported to be haunted by the ghost of the unfortunate teacher. Young farmhands, traveling home on still• summer evenings, have often thought they heard his voice in the distance, singing a sad psalm in some secluded• corner of Sleepy Hollow.

Glossary

- **decay:** a bad condition
- **means:** ways
- **secluded:** hidden; quiet
- **spirited away:** made to disappear; taken away
- **still:** quiet

After Reading

Personal Response

1 Before you finished reading, did you guess how the story would end? Tell the class.

2 Did you like the ending of the story? Would you prefer the story to end in a different way? Work with a partner and together think of an alternative ending.

3 Now that you have read the story, do you think Sleepy Hollow is a good name for the place where the events take place?

4 In your opinion who or what did Ichabod love most? What did he want most of all from life? Did he achieve his ambition?

5 What did you learn about the legend of the Headless Horseman? Can you write his story?

6 At the end of Van Tassel's party Ichabod goes to talk to Katrina. Why is this meeting so important? Why doesn't the author show us this scene? How do we know that Ichabod left 'looking quite upset'? Did anybody see him?

7 If you could be a character in the story, who would you like to be?

After Reading

Comprehension

1 **Work with a partner. One of you reads the A Questions and the other the B Questions. (Make sure you know the answers to your own set of questions.)**

A Questions

What is the other name given to the town of Greensburgh?
What was the nationality of the town's original settlers?
Where did Ichabod Crane come from?
How did Ichabod meet Katrina Van Tassel?
What was Ichabod's job?
What was the title of Ichabod's favourite book?

B Questions

Where did many husbands tarry on market day?
What did the Horseman of Sleepy Hollow lose and did he ever find it again?
What did Ichabod do on his way home at night to drive away evil spirits?
Where did Ichabod Crane go after he left Sleepy Hollow?
What was Ichabod's job at the end of the story?
What happened to Ichabod's favourite book and his poems?

2 **Work with your partner. Write four more questions about the story. Find another pair and ask them your questions.**

3 Tick (✓) true (T) or false (F).

	T	F
a) The narrator of the story is dead.	☐	☐
b) The Sleepy Hollow Boys are students from a local school.	☐	☐
c) The Headless Horseman is the ghost of a soldier killed in the war.	☐	☐
d) The story of Ichabod Crane took place around 20 years ago.	☐	☐
e) The parents of Ichabod's pupils gave him food and a place to stay.	☐	☐
f) Ichabod enjoyed reading love stories.	☐	☐
g) Katrina Van Tassel was twenty-five years old.	☐	☐
h) Brom Bones usually visited Katrina on Sunday nights.	☐	☐

4 Match these sentences from the story with their meanings.

a) ☐ The whole school was turned loose an hour before the usual time.
b) ☐ He managed to do justice to every dainty.
c) ☐ He prided himself on his dancing.
d) ☐ His heart began to sink.
e) ☐ He hoped to give his companion the slip.

1 He felt lost and without hope.
2 He ate everything.
3 He tried to escape.
4 All the children went home early.
5 He thought he was a good dancer.

After Reading

Characters

1 Who are these people ? Work with a partner and write the missing names.

a) He had a nickname but his real name was Abraham.

....

b) He wrote a book called 'History of New England Witchcraft'.

....

c) After he died, they found an account of the events at Sleepy Hollow among his papers.

....

d) During the Revolutionary War a cannon ball knocked his head off.

....

e) He was a Dutch farmer who used to be a mad horse rider.

....

2 Read the sentences below. Who do they describe: Ichabod or Brom?

a) He believes he is a good dancer. ....
b) He wears a fur cap with a fox's tail. ....
c) The horse he rides is called Daredevil. ....
d) He owns a black suit. ....
e) He has broad shoulders. ....
f) The horse he rides is called Gunpowder. ....
g) He has three or four close companions. ....
h) He is thin even though he eats a lot. ....

3 Which adjectives best describe Katrina? Discuss in pairs, giving evidence for your choices.

crafty clever helpful spoilt honest foolish sweet flirtatious well-off kind gracious

4 Work with two other partners. Imagine that you are a police team investigating the disappearance of Ichabod Crane.

a) Write down what questions you want to ask Brom, Katrina and Baltus.
b) Now find three students to be Brom, Katrina and Baltus.
c) Ask Brom, Katrina and Baltus your questions.
d) Discuss the answers and compare the information.
e) Tell the class what you think happened to Ichabod.

5 Who in the story might say the following words? Match the sentences with the people. Explain your choices.

Katrina Baltus Van Tassel Ichabod Brom

a) 'Believe me. I know. I've read many books on the subject. I'm an expert.' ....
b) 'I'm sorry if I gave you the wrong impression. You see my heart belongs to another.' ....
c) 'So, he doesn't want to fight. That's a pity, because I'm going to make him suffer for what he is doing.' ....
d) 'What a lovely time we're all having. Don't be shy. Help yourself to some more pumpkin pie.' ....

After Reading

Plot and Theme

1 **Many stories are told in *The Legend of Sleepy Hollow*. Can you complete the information about some of these stories by matching the two halves of the sentences below?**

a) ☐ In one story a Dutchman called Doffue Martling nearly captured …
b) ☐ The narrator of The Legend of Sleepy Hollow is …
c) ☐ Ichabod Crane told the old women tales about …
d) ☐ They say that a German doctor put …
e) ☐ In Brom Bones's story he raced …
f) ☐ They told a story about a woman in white who haunted …
g) ☐ According to another story, an old Indian chief held …

1 omens and terrible sights and sounds.
2 Raven Rock, having died there in the snow.
3 a British ship during the war.
4 against the Headless Horseman in order to win a bowl of punch.
5 his powwows in Sleepy Hollow.
6 a man called Diedrich Knickerbocker.
7 a spell on Sleepy Hollow during the early days of the settlement.

2 **Say what happened to:**

a) a certain old gentleman during the Battle of White Plains.
b) the man they called old Brouwer.
c) the soldier who was killed by a cannon ball.

3 Which of the following themes do you think is present in *The Legend of Sleepy Hollow*? Tick (✓).

- ☐ Man's selfishness and greed.
- ☐ The role of superstition and the supernatural.
- ☐ The dangers of jealousy.
- ☐ The power of storytelling.
- ☐ The importance of nature.
- ☐ Dreams versus reality.
- ☐ The power of love to overcome all difficulties.

4 Do you agree with any of the following statements?

	agree	don't agree	not sure
The money someone has is more important than their social class.			
We shouldn't believe everything we read.			
People are usually motivated by greed.			
Educated people always succeed better in life than uneducated people.			
Having a vivid imagination can be dangerous.			

5 What ideas or messages do you think the author wants to convey to his readers? Can you find examples in the story to support the statements in Exercise 4?

After Reading

Language

1 **Read the groups of words below and circle the odd-one-out.**

a) ginger cakes puddings doughnuts smoked beef
b) stockings buttons coats breeches petticoats
c) pies apples peaches plums pears
d) turkeys ducks pigeons bullfrogs geese
e) wheat cider corn rye oats

2 **Using a dictionary, work with a partner to label this picture of Gunpowder. Use the words from the box.**

mane bridle stirrups whip tail girth reins hoof

3 The little valley near Tarry Town is one of the 'quietest' places in the whole world. Work with a partner. Take turns to ask and answer these questions.

- Which is the noisiest place you know?
- Which is the friendliest place?
- Which is the most beautiful place?
- Which is the cleanest place?

Now, make up some similar questions of your own and ask your partner to answer them.

4 Find words in the box that have a similar meaning to the underlined words in these sentences.

horse	magic	jump	tales	gigantic	apparition	prank

a) Every little sound at that witching hour stirred Ichabod's imagination. ....

b) Brom had no alternative but to think up some unpleasant practical joke to play on his rival. ....

c) This legend has provided material for many wild stories. ....

d) It is only fair to give you a true description of my hero and his steed. ....

e) He saw the spectre standing up in his stirrups, in the act of throwing his head at him. ....

f) The shadowy shape started to move, and with a leap it stood in the middle of the road. ....

g) He appeared to be a horseman of massive dimensions. ....

After Reading

Test

1 **Read the questions and tick (✓) the most suitable answers.**

a) **Why is Greensburgh better known as Tarry Town?**
1 ☐ It was named after a man called Mr Tarry.
2 ☐ The wives of that area liked the name.
3 ☐ On market days husbands tarried in the local tavern.

b) **Why was it difficult for Ichabod to gain Katrina's affections?**
1 ☐ Her parents did not like him.
2 ☐ Ichabod's rivals watched him angrily and did not let him speak to Katrina.
3 ☐ Katrina was spoilt and had many admirers to choose from.

c) **What did Ichabod do when he first saw the figure by the edge of the stream?**
1 ☐ He turned his horse around and ran away.
2 ☐ He greeted the figure in a welcoming voice.
3 ☐ He closed his eyes and sang a hymn.

d) **What did the village people find when they searched for Ichabod?**
1 ☐ They found a bundle containing all Ichabod's worldly effects.
2 ☐ They found the remains of a large pumpkin on the bank of the stream.
3 ☐ They found Gunpowder eating grass and still wearing his bridle and saddle.

2 Answer the questions.

a) In which war did the Headless Horseman lose his head?
b) What did Ichabod use to punish the troublemakers in his class?
c) How do we know that Katrina was 'a bit of a flirt'?
d) How did people know that Brom was visiting Katrina on Sunday nights?
e) Why did Brom like to ride nasty horses?
f) Where did Ichabod meet the Headless Horseman?
g) Why was Ichabod so worried about losing his horse's saddle?
h) What happened to Ichabod?

3 Tick (✓) true (T) or false (F).

	T	F
a) Diedrich Knickerbocker is the narrator.	☐	☐
b) Ichabod instructed the children to paint and draw.	☐	☐
c) Brom taught a dog to dance and introduced it as a rival of Ichabod's.	☐	☐
d) Ichabod borrowed a horse called Daredevil from Hans Van Ripper.	☐	☐
e) Ichabod was impressed by the huge display of cakes at the Van Tassel mansion.	☐	☐
f) A group of musicians played while the party guests danced.	☐	☐
g) When the dancing was over, everyone went home.	☐	☐
h) Brom beat the Headless Horseman in a race and won a bowl of punch.	☐	☐

After Reading

Project

1 Here are some headlines from the Sleepy Hollow newspapers after Ichabod disappeared. What do you think they refer to?

a **Missing Horse Safe**

b **SLEEPY RESIDENTS COMPLAIN TO EDUCATION AUTHORITIES**

c **HORSEMAN CLAIMS ANOTHER VICTIM**

d **PUMPKIN CLUE TO TEACHER'S DISAPPEARANCE**

e **Farmer Claims Compensation For Damaged Saddle**

WEB 2 Look at some newspaper headlines on the Internet. Invent some similar headlines of your own.

3 Choose a headline of your own or from the list above. Work with a partner and write a short newspaper article to match the headline.

4 In groups edit and correct the story and decide on a suitable illustration. Bring all the stories together in a class newspaper.